The King's Race
and other stories

Nelson

Nelson Thornes Ltd
Delta Place
27 Bath Road
CHELTENHAM
GL53 7TH
United Kingdom

© Thomas Nelson and Sons Ltd 1991
Editorial Consultant: Donna Bailey
'The King's race' was written by Penny Hegarty and illustrated by Joyce Smith
and David Dowland
'The Emperor's clothes' was was adapted from Hans Christian Andersens's story by
Joan Wyatt and illustrated by Doffy Weir
'Rich man, poor man' was written by Joan Wyatt and illustrated by Tony Smith

First published by Macmillan Education Ltd 1987

This edition published by Thomas Nelson and Sons Ltd 1992

Reprinted in 2001 by Nelson Thornes Ltd

ISBN 0–17–400611–X
06 07 08 / 20 19 18 17

Printed in Croatia by Zrinski

The King's Race

George Frog could not swim.
He kicked with his big back legs and
pushed the water with his arms,
but still he could **not** swim.
"I don't know what to do about you,
George," said his mother sadly.
"All frogs can swim. You must try harder."
So George tried again.

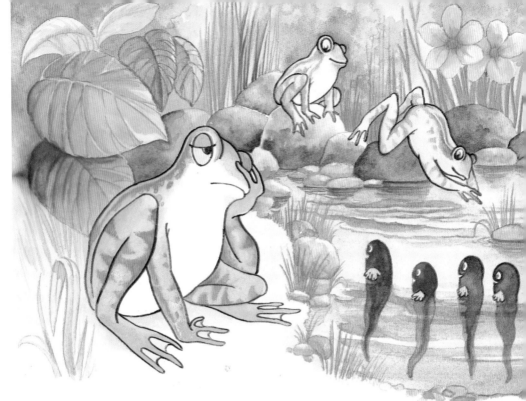

He splashed and splashed.
The water got up his nose and made him cough.
The water got in his eyes and made him blink.
"It's no good," said George.
"I've tried as hard as I can,
but I just can't swim."
So he sat sadly by the side of the pond
all alone and watched the other frogs
swim and play and dive down deep
in the cool green water.

"Come on George," cried the tadpoles.
"It's the King's Race today.
Come and swim with us."
They laughed and swished their long
black tails in the water.

George tried not to cry.
The King was coming to watch the race and
there would be a big party afterwards,
with games on the grass and lots to eat.
But only the frogs who swam in the race
could go to the party.

It was a very important race.
There was a row of rushes to show
where the frogs must start.
When the King waved his green flag,
they would all dive in and set off.
The first frog to reach the big willow tree
would be the winner.

"I don't want to see the race,"
said George sadly. "I will go and hide."
So George hopped away and
hid in the long grass.

A dragonfly was sitting on a leaf in the sun. "Hello," she said. "You will be late for the race."

"I can't go in the race," said George. "I can't swim."

The dragonfly laughed and laughed. "Don't be silly," she said. "All frogs can swim."

"One — two — three — **go**!" said the King and waved his flag.

"The race has started," said the dragonfly. "I must go and watch," and she flew off to the pond.

George sat down in the grass again.
He was so sad.
It was very hard not to cry.
    Just then George heard a terrible noise.
It was right behind him and it was very loud.
It was a horrible huffing, puffing noise.
George jumped up in fright.
Then he saw it was a dog,
a horrible furry brown dog.
    "Oh!" said George and jumped up
with a huge leap.

The dog saw the frog jump out of the grass. He barked loudly and ran after George.

"No! No!" cried George, jumping higher and higher.

"Woof! Woof!" barked the dog, running after George.

"Help! Help!" cried George, jumping and jumping and jumping until **splash!** he jumped right into the pond.

"Woof! Woof!" barked the dog, running into the pond after George.

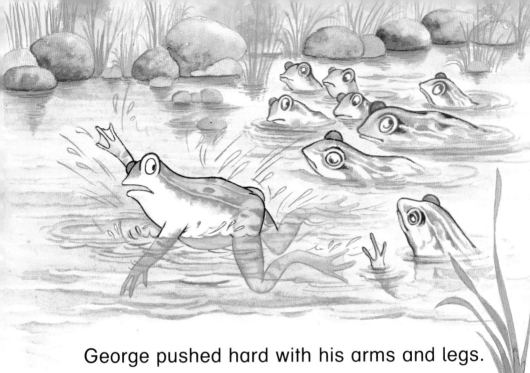

George pushed hard with his arms and legs.
He must get away.
He must not let the dog get near him.
The water splashed in his face.
It splashed him all over and it got up his nose,
but George did not care. He **must** get away!

Just in front of him George saw
lots of other frogs.

"Quick!" shouted George as he swam past.
"There is a big brown dog coming this way."
The other frogs were so surprised
they nearly forgot to swim.

"Look at George!" cried the frogs.
"He can swim!" And he could!
But George did not stop swimming until
he got to the big willow tree
at the side of the pond.

"I will rest here," he said and
climbed out of the water.

"Well done, George," said the King.
"You are the best swimmer of all and today
you have won the King's Race."

The Emperor's clothes

Once upon a time there was an Emperor.
He liked his golden crown and
he loved his fine clothes.
He didn't think about anything else.
All his people bowed down low
when they came to see him.

"Yes, your majesty," they said.
"No, your majesty," and
he always had his own way.

One day the golden buttons on
his coat wouldn't do up.
He looked at himself in the mirror.
   "Do you think I am getting fat?" he said.
   "Oh no, your majesty," said the lords.
   "Your coat has shrunk," said the ladies.
   "I need some new clothes," said the Emperor.
"At once. Today. Send for a tailor," he said.

Just then two strangers stepped forward.
They bowed low.

"Your majesty," they said. "We make clothes
from magic cloth. Only wise people can see
them. Silly people can't see them at all."

Now the Emperor thought he was very wise.

"Show me your cloth," he said.

The strangers brought a heavy box.
They threw open the lid.
The lords and ladies looked inside,
but the box was empty.
The strangers pretended to lift out
a roll of cloth.

"Look," they said. "Do you like the colours?"
The lords and ladies looked at each other.
They did not want to seem silly.
They all pretended to see the cloth.

"What blues," said the lords.

"What lovely reds," said the ladies.

The strangers smiled.

"Do you like it your majesty?" they said.

The Emperor could not see the cloth either, but he did not want to look silly.

"What silver," he said. "What gold."

The strangers smiled.

"How wise you are your majesty," they said. "Anyone can see that.

Shall we make a new suit for you from this gold and silver cloth?"

"Please do," said the Emperor.

So the most important lord gave the strangers
some money for the new suit and
the strangers took their heavy box away
and set to work.

Soon the whole town knew about
the Emperor's clothes.

"Only wise people will see them," they said.
"Silly people won't see them at all when
the Emperor walks through the town."

The strangers worked hard.
They cut the air with sharp scissors.
They sewed nothing with silver needles.
At night they kept sixteen candles burning.

"The strangers are working night and day,"
said the people in the town.

The most important lord went to see
the new clothes being made.

"We are just sewing on the golden buttons,"
said the strangers. "The Emperor's suit
is nearly ready now."

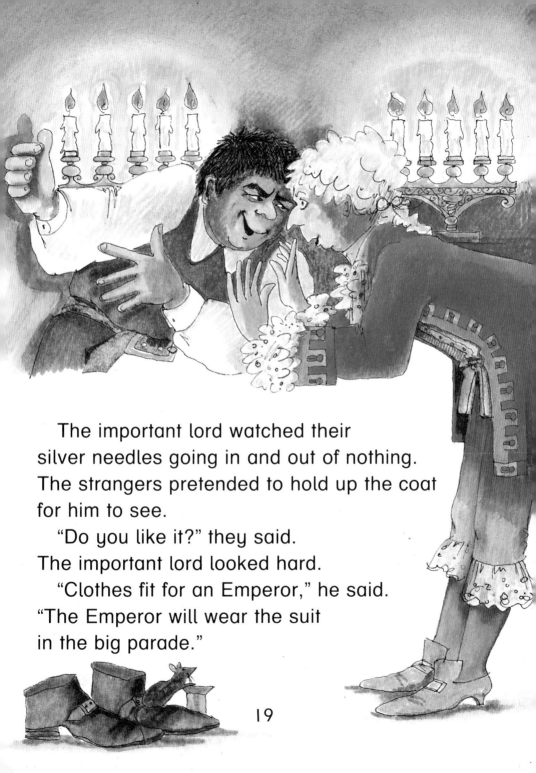

The important lord watched their
silver needles going in and out of nothing.
The strangers pretended to hold up the coat
for him to see.

"Do you like it?" they said.
The important lord looked hard.

"Clothes fit for an Emperor," he said.
"The Emperor will wear the suit
in the big parade."

19

At last the day of the parade came.
Everyone was getting ready.
The strangers carried their heavy box
to the palace.
They took the clothes out one by one.
   The Emperor put on his best purple underpants.
Then the strangers helped him put on
his new shirt, his new trousers and
his new coat.
   "How well they fit," said the Emperor.
"I will wear my golden crown as well," he said.

So he put on his crown and
went to join the parade.
All the people were waiting in the streets.
The children had a holiday from school.
They all wanted to see
the Emperor's new clothes.
First came the band playing loudly on
their trumpets and drums.
Then came the lords and ladies
dressed in their best clothes.
The people cheered. They waved their flags.
Then at last came the Emperor.

Everyone looked at him.
No one wanted to seem silly.
   "What colours," they said.
   "What reds and blues."
   "What lovely new clothes."
But just then the Emperor
passed by the children.
   "What new clothes?" said the smallest child.
"He's not wearing anything but his crown and
purple underpants!" and she began to laugh.

Then the other children began to laugh and
the other people began to laugh and
the lords and ladies began to laugh.

"She's right," they all said, laughing.

Then the Emperor knew he had been
very silly and not wise at all.
He ran back into his palace and
from that day on he didn't think about
his fine clothes any more.

And do you know what?

The strangers were never seen in the town again.

Rich man, poor man

Once a rich man lived next door to a poor man.
The rich man had a big house,
the poor man had a small house.
The rich man's front door was painted
a bright red, but the poor man's door
was old and shabby.

The poor man was saving up.
He wanted to buy a bike and a trailer.
Then he could go to the market
to buy fruit and vegetables.
He could put the fruit and
vegetables in the trailer.
Then he could take them round to
people's houses and sell them.

He got up early every morning and
worked hard all day.
Every evening he put his savings
into a little leather bag.
Soon he would be as rich as the man next door
and he could paint his door bright red too.

One day the rich man gave a party.
He invited all his friends but
he did not invite the poor man.
The poor man stood at his door and
watched all the grand people arrive.
He watched all the good food being carried in.
The food smelled so good that
he could almost taste it.
He smelled the chicken and rice.
He smelled the curry and peppers.
He smelled the fish and chips.
He licked his lips. He did feel hungry.

The rich man saw the poor man looking at
the food being taken in for his party, but
he did not say, "Come and join us."
Instead he sat with his friends and
tasted all the food.

But something was wrong.
None of the food tasted quite right.
His friends were not happy and
soon they all left and the party was over.

The rich man sat by himself in his big house.

"What was wrong with my food?" he said.

Then he had an idea.

"The poor man spoilt my party," he said.
"He sniffed all the goodness from my food.
He stood and sniffed the chicken and rice.
He sniffed the curry and peppers.
He sniffed the fish and chips.
I will take him before the judge."

The next day the rich man
told the judge his story.
The judge listened and looked at the poor man.
  "Did you sniff the food?" he said.
  "Yes," said the poor man.
What else could he say?
He could still smell the chicken and rice.
He could still smell the curry and peppers.
He could still smell the fish and chips.
And he was still hungry.

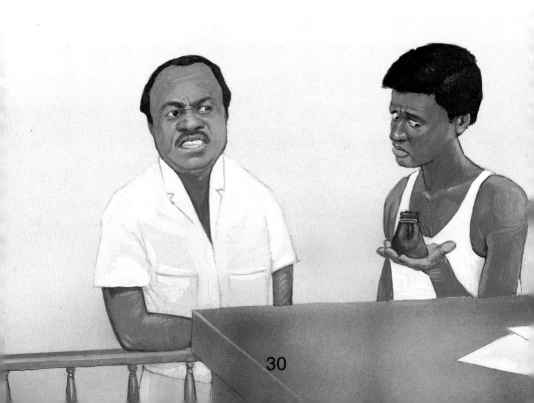

"You must pay a fine," said the judge.
So the poor man took out his little leather bag.
The money he had saved clinked sadly.
The poor man was sad.
He would never be able to buy a bike now.
The rich man held out his hand for the money.
   "Stop!" said the judge.
Then he said to the rich man,
"You must only have the sound of the money
because he only had the smell of the food."

The rich man turned away.
The poor man shook his little leather bag.
Soon he would buy his bike.
Soon he would buy the trailer.
Soon he would fill his trailer full of
fruit and vegetables.
And soon he would paint his door a bright red.
Then he would have a big party and
invite everyone – even the man next door.